DAVID AND GOLIATH

Long ago, there was a tall, handsome

boy called David living in the land of

Israel. Many times, when was

watching over his father's , a

 or a came to take a lamb.

 was scared of the wild beasts,

but he always ran to help the .

He would take his from his belt and send a large flying at the  or the to kill it. Then he rescued the lamb.

In those days, was the king of Israel. At first, ruled well and with God's help he won many battles against Israel's enemies, the .

But 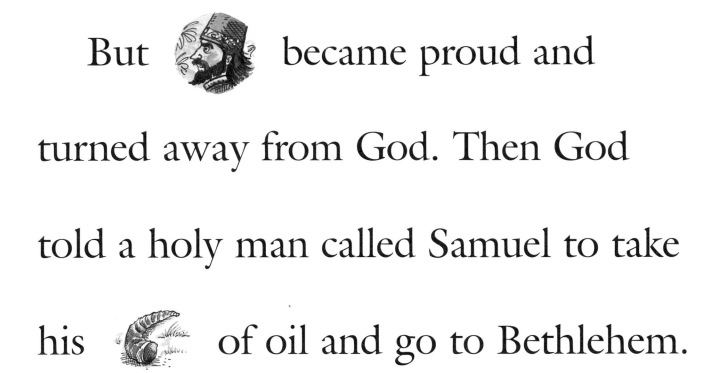 became proud and turned away from God. Then God told a holy man called Samuel to take his  of oil and go to Bethlehem.

"There you must find , the son of Jesse," God told . "Tell him he will be Israel's next king."

When  found in Bethlehem, he poured oil out of his over 's head to show that he was God's chosen one.

Now  had bad dreams, sent by

God to punish him for his pride. He said to his , "Find someone to play the for me. The music might help me to sleep."

The went to . He was Israel's best -player, who later wrote the Psalms, famous songs in praise of God.

was brought to  and when he played his to the king, the music drove away the dreams and  was able to sleep.

Once again, the made war on the Israelites and and his army marched out to fight them. When the two armies were face to face, a giant of a man called Goliath stepped forward.

He shook his great  at  's army and called out, "Send one man out to fight me. If he kills me, the

 will become Israel's . But

if I kill him, then you shall be

of the ."

No one in 's army was brave

enough to fight , until one day

 , visiting his brothers nearby,

heard  's words. He said to

 , "I will fight  ."

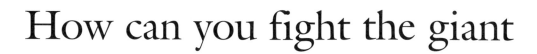 said, "But you are only a boy.

How can you fight the giant ?"

Then told that he had

killed both a  and a in the past to protect his . "Let me do it. God will help me if I fight against  ."

 said to  , "Put on my

 when you go out to fight." But

 's was too heavy. So

went without it. On his way to fight,

 gathered for his .

When  saw , he laughed

and boasted, "I will kill you and feed

your body to the ."

was not afraid. "You may be great in size," he said to , "but the God of Israel is on my side. Today you and all the will be destroyed."

Then put a in his , whirled it round his head, and let it fly at great speed at .

The hit 's head with great force and he toppled to the ground. had killed him.

Then cut off 's head with the giant's own . Seeing this, the ran away, chased by  's army into the wilderness.

All the people of Israel thanked for saving them. They made up songs about his defeat of , and cheered when passed by.

 took into his own

house and became as close as a

brother to 's son, Jonathan.

 became jealous of after

his victory, because the people loved

him so much. Twice, in a rage,

threw a at , but each time

he missed. This made believe

that God was taking care of him.

But had to run away or he

would have been killed.

Later,  married 's daughter, Michal. He remained friends with Jonathan, but was still not safe from 's rage.

Again  had to run away and he was hunted like an animal by  's army . Eventually, during yet another battle with the , both  and his son Jonathan were killed. Then became king, but it was many years before he was able to defeat the for the final time.